The Complete Guitar Player Children's Songs

by Arthur Dick.

London/N...../Madrid

Exclusive Distributors:
Music Sales Limited
8/9 Frith Street,
London W1V 5TZ, England.
Music Sales Pty Limited
120 Rothschild Avenue,
Rosebery, NSW 2018, Australia.

This book © Copyright 1994 by Wise Publications
Order No. AM91100
ISBN 0-7119-3431-2

Compiled by Peter Evans
Music arranged by Arthur Dick
Music processed by The Pitts

Printed in the United Kingdom by
Printwise (Haverhill) Limited, Suffolk

Your Guarantee of Quality
As publishers, we strive to produce every book to the
highest commercial standards.
The music has been freshly engraved and the book has been
carefully designed to minimise awkward page turns and to make
playing from it a real pleasure.
Particular care has been given to specifying acid-free, neutral-sized
paper made from pulps which have not been elemental chlorine bleached.
This pulp is from farmed sustainable forests and was produced with
special regard for the environment.
Throughout, the printing and binding have been planned to ensure a sturdy,
attractive publication which should give years of enjoyment.
If your copy fails to meet our high standards, please inform us
and we will gladly replace it.

Music Sales' complete catalogue describes thousands of titles and is
available in full colour sections by subject, direct from Music Sales Limited.
Please state your areas of interest and send a cheque/postal order for £1.50 for postage to:
Music Sales Limited, Newmarket Road, Bury St. Edmunds, Suffolk IP33 3YB.

Amazing Grace Traditional.

3/4 Rhythm / Simple arpeggio
See Course Book No.1 Page 25.

Verse 2
'Twas grace that taught my heart to fear
And grace my fear relieved
How precious did that grace appear
The hour I first believed.

Verse 3
Through many dangers, toils and snares
We have already come
'Twas grace that brought us safe thus far
And grace will lead us home.

Verse 4
When we've been there ten thousand years
Bright shining as the sun
We've no less days to sing God's praise
Than when we first begun.

Verse 5
Amazing grace, how sweet the sound
That saved a wretch like me
I once was lost but now I'm found
Was blind, but now I see.

We All Stand Together

Words & Music by Paul McCartney.

3/4 Rhythm / Bass-strum
See Course Book No.1 Pages 14 and 22.

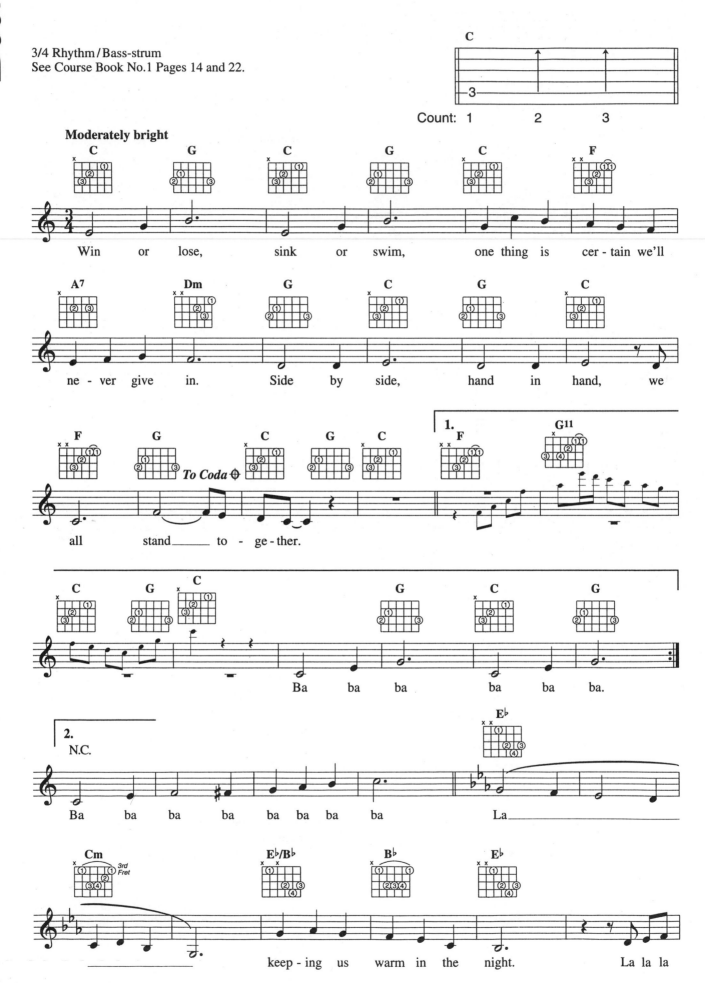

Count: 1   2   3

Moderately bright

Win or lose, sink or swim, one thing is cer - tain we'll

ne - ver give in. Side by side, hand in hand, we

To Coda ⊕

all stand_____ to - ge - ther.

1. G11

Ba ba ba ba ba ba.

2. N.C.

Ba ba ba ba ba ba ba ba La_____

_____ keep - ing us warm in the night. La la la

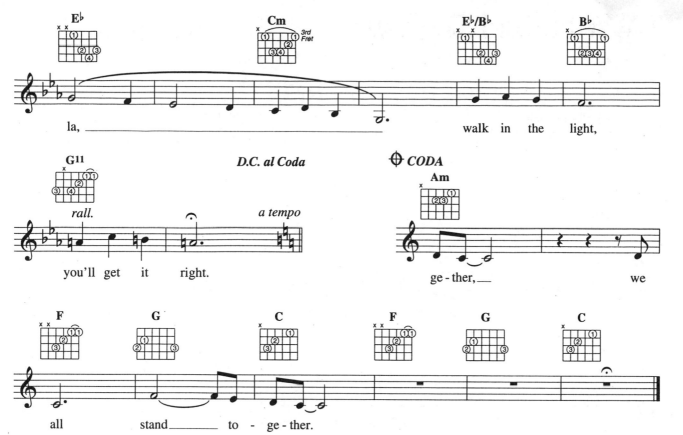

la, _____ walk in the light,

rall.   *a tempo*   *D.C. al Coda*   ⊕ *CODA*

you'll get it right.   ge - ther, ___   we

all   stand _____ to - ge - ther.

Verse 2
Play the game, fight the fight
But what's the point on a beautiful night
Arm in arm, hand in hand
We all stand together.

Verse 3
Win or lose, sink or swim
One thing is certain we'll never give in
Arm in arm, hand in hand
We all stand together.

I Wanna Be Like You

Words & Music by Richard M. Sherman & Robert B. Sherman.

4/4 Rhythm / Strumming
See Course Book No.1 Page 14.

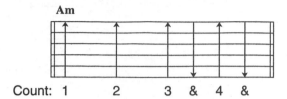

Count: 1   2   3 & 4 &

Now   I'm   the   king   of   the   swing - ers,   the   jun - gle   V.   I.

P.   I've   reached   the   top   and   had   to   stop   and   that's what's both - er - in'

me.   I   wan - na   be   a   man,   man - cub,   and   stroll   right   in - to

town,   And   be   just   like   the   oth - er   men,   I'm   tired   of   mon - key - in'

CHORUS

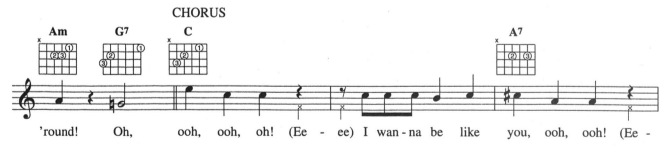

'round!   Oh,   ooh,   ooh,   oh!   (Ee - ee)   I   wan - na   be   like   you,   ooh,   ooh!   (Ee -

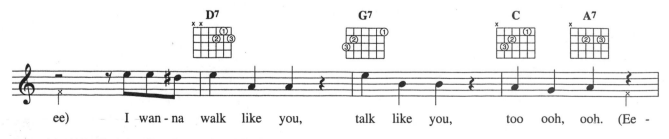

ee)   I   wan - na   walk   like   you,   talk   like   you,   too ooh,   ooh.   (Ee -

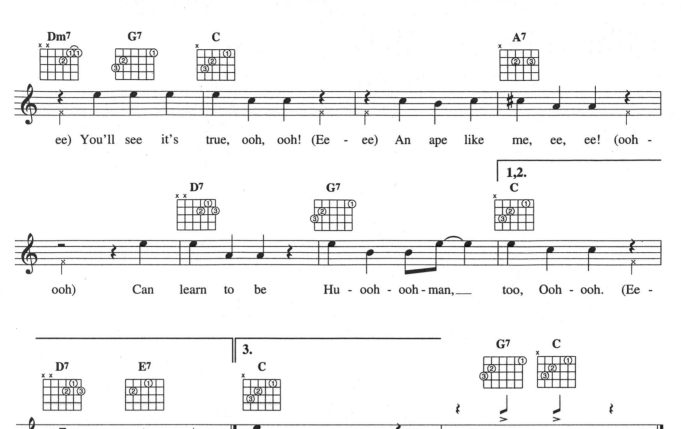

ee) You'll see it's true, ooh, ooh! (Ee - ee) An ape like me, ee, ee! (ooh -

ooh) Can learn to be Hu - ooh - ooh - man, ___ too, Ooh - ooh. (Ee -

ee) 2. Don't too, Ooh - ooh. (Ee - ee)

Verse 2
Don't try to kid me, mancub
And don't get in a stew
What I desire is man's red fire
So I can be like you.
Give me the secret, mancub
Just clue me what to do
Give me the pow'r of man's red flow'r
And make my dream come true!

Verse 3
I'll ape your mannerisms
We'll be a set of twins
No-one will know where mancub ends
And orangutan begins.
And when I eat bananas
I won't peel them with my feet
'Cause I'll become a man, mancub
And learn some "ettikeet"!

A Windmill In Old Amsterdam

Words & Music by Ted Dicks & Myles Rudge.

3/4 Rhythm / Bass-strum
See Course Book No.1 Pages 16 and 17.

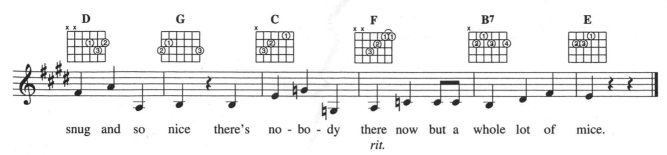

snug and so nice there's no-bo-dy there now but a whole lot of mice.

rit.

Verse 2
The mouse he got lonesome he took him a wife
A windmill with mice in is hardly surprisin'
She sang ev'ry morning "How lucky I am
Living in a windmill in old Amsterdam."

Verse 3
First they had triplets and then they had quins
A windmill with quins in, triplets and twins in
They sang ev'ry morning "How lucky I am
Living in a windmill in old Amsterdam."

Verse 4
The daughters got married and so did the sons
The windmill had christ'nings when no one was list'nin'
They all sang in chorus "How lucky I am
Living in a windmill in old Amsterdam."

Old MacDonald Had A Farm Traditional.

4/4 Rhythm / Bass-strum
See Course Book No.1 Pages 14 and 22.

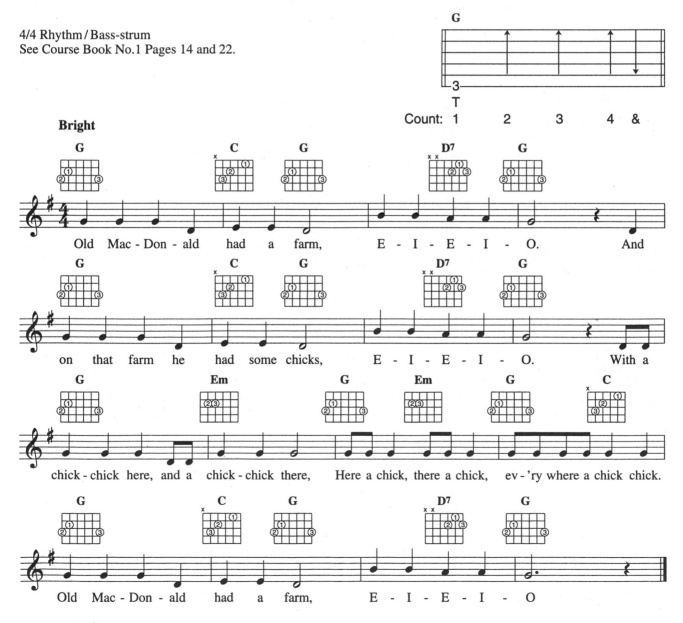

Sing   Words & Music by Joe Raposo.

4/4 Rhythm / Strumming
See Course Book No.1 Page 14.

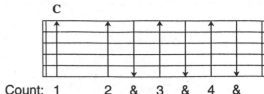

Count: 1   2 & 3 & 4 &

Sing!   Sing a song.   Sing out loud,   sing out

strong.   Sing of good things, not bad;

Sing of hap-py, not sad.   Sing!   Sing a

song.   Make it sim-ple to last your whole life long._____ Don't

wor-ry that it's not good e-nough for an-y-one else to hear.   Sing!   Sing a

song!_____   La la do la da, La da la do la da, La da da la do la da.

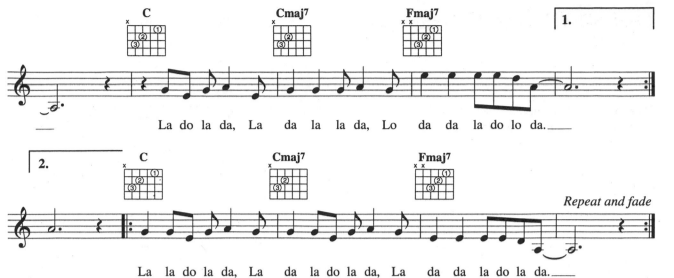

La la do la da, La da la da, Lo da da la do lo da.____

La la do la da, La da la do la da, La da da la do la da.____

Mary Had A Little Lamb Traditional.

2/4 Rhythm / Bass-strum
See Course Book No.1 Page 22.

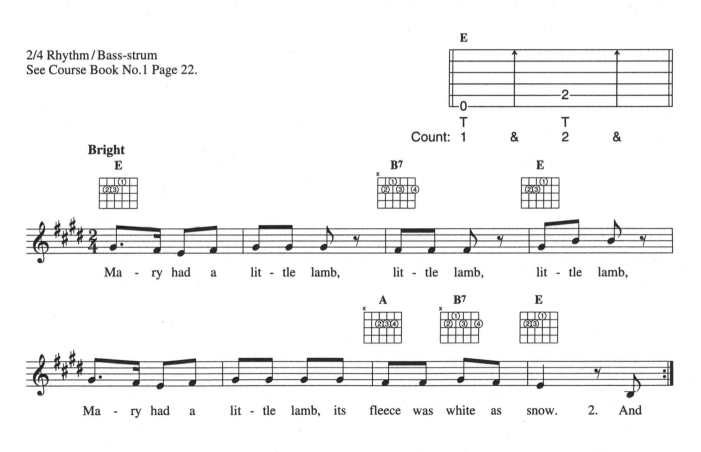

Verse 2
And ev'rywhere that Mary went
Mary went, Mary went
Ev'rywhere that Mary went
The lamb was sure to go.

Verse 3
It followed her to school one day
School one day, school one day
It followed her to school one day
Which was against the rules.

Verse 4
It made the children laugh and play
Laugh and play, laugh and play
It made the children laugh and play
To see a lamb at school.

Bye Bye Love

Words & Music by Felice & Boudleaux Bryant.

4/4 Rhythm / Strumming / Swing / Lively
See Course Book No.2 Pages 5-8.

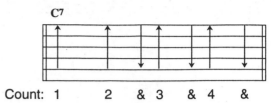

Count: 1   2 & 3 & 4 &

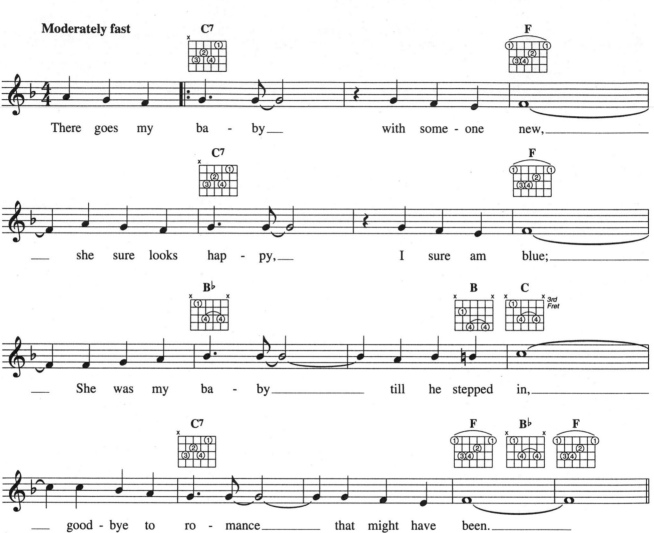

Moderately fast

There goes my ba - by ___ with some - one new, ___

___ she sure looks hap - py, ___ I sure am blue; ___

___ She was my ba - by ___ till he stepped in, ___

___ good - bye to ro - mance ___ that might have been. ___

CHORUS

Bye bye love,   Bye bye, hap - pi - ness, ___   Hel - lo

lone - li - ness, ___ I think I'm gon - na cry; ___   Bye bye

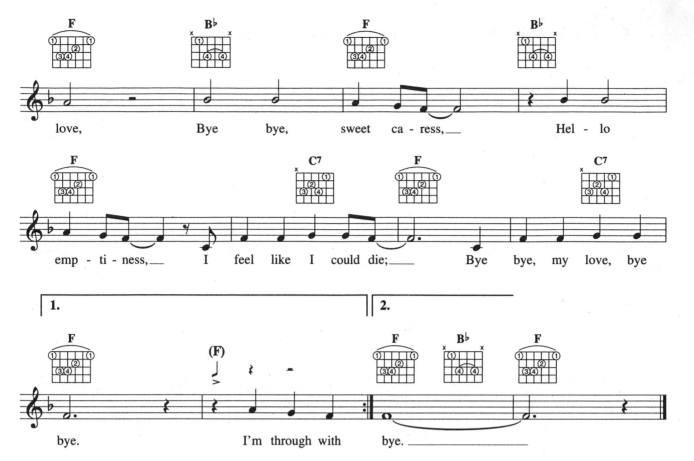

| F | B♭ | F | B♭ |

love,　　　　Bye　bye,　　sweet ca - ress,___　　　　Hel - lo

| F | C7 | F | C7 |

emp - ti - ness,___　I　feel　like　I　could　die;___　　Bye　bye,　my　love,　bye

1. | **2.**

| F | (F) | F | B♭ | F |

bye.　　　　　　　I'm　through　with　　bye. _____

Verse 2

I'm through with romance, I'm through with love
I'm through with counting the stars above
And here's the reason that I'm so free
My lovin' baby is through with me.

Thank U Very Much

Words & Music by Michael McGear.

2/4 Rhythm / Strumming
See Course Book No.2 Page 10.

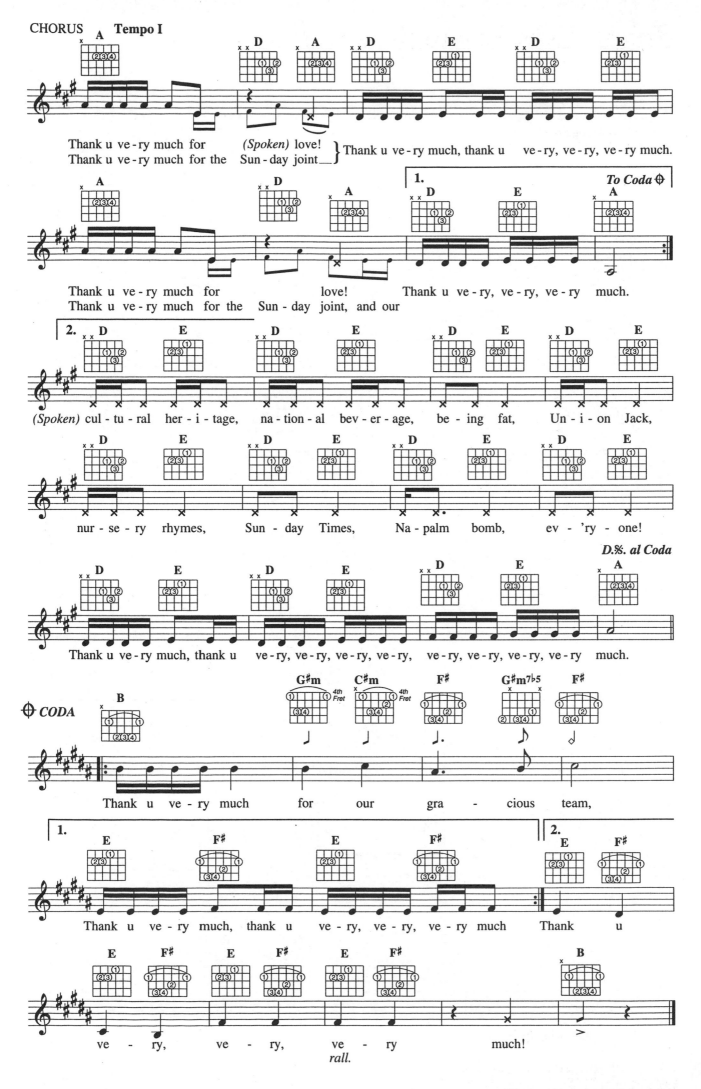

Bright Eyes
Words & Music by Mike Batt.

4/4 Rhythm / Arpeggio
See Course Book No.2 Page 20.

CHORUS

Bright eyes burn - ing like fire,

Bright eyes how can you close and fail,

How can the light that burned so bright - ly sud - den - ly burn so pale?

1.
Bright eyes.

2.
Bright eyes.

To Coda ⊕

D.%. al Coda
(no repeat)

Bright eyes

⊕ *CODA*

Continue arpeggios

poco rit.

Verse 2
Is it a kind of shadow
Reaching into the night
Wandering over the hills unseen
Or is it a dream?

There's a high wind in the trees
A cold sound in the air
And nobody ever knows where you go
And where do you start
Oh, oh, into the dark.

I'd Like To Teach The World To Sing

Words & Music by Roger Cook, Roger Greenaway, Billy Backer & Billy Davis.

4/4 Rhythm / Strumming / Swing
See Course Book No.2 Pages 5 - 8.

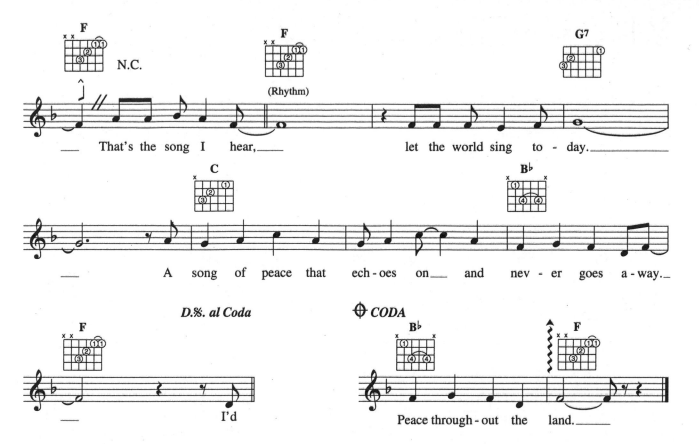

N.C.

That's the song I hear,_____ let the world sing to - day._____

A song of peace that ech - oes on___ and nev - er goes a - way.___

D.%. al Coda

⊕ *CODA*

_____ I'd

Peace through - out the land._____

Yellow Submarine
Words & Music by John Lennon & Paul McCartney.

4/4 Rhythm / Strumming / Swing
See Course Book No.2 Pages 5 and 10.

20

yel - low sub - ma - rine, yel - low sub - ma - rine. And our friends are all a-

board ma - ny more of them live next door, And the

band_____ be - gins to play: Brass cue

green In our yel - low sub - ma - rine.

yel - low sub - ma - rine. We all live in a yel - low sub - ma - rine, yel - low sub - ma - rine,

yel - low sub - ma - rine. We all live in a yel - low sub - ma - rine, yel - low sub - ma - rine,

On ※
We all live in a yellow submarine
Yellow submarine, yellow submarine
We all live in a yellow submarine
Yellow submarine, yellow submarine.

As we live a life of ease
Ev'ry one of us has all we need
Sky of blue and sea of green
In our yellow submarine.

21

Little White Duck

Words by Walt Barrows. Music by Bernard Zaritzky.

4/4 Rhythm / Alternating thumb
See Course Book No.2 Page 23.

Verse 2
There's a little green frog swimming in the water
A little green frog doing what he oughter
He jumped right off of the lily pad
That the little duck bit and he said
"I'm glad I'm a little green frog swimming in the water"
Glumph, glumph, glumph.

Verse 3
There's a little black bug floating in the water
A little black bug doing what he oughter
He tickled the frog on the lily pad
That the little duck bit and he said
"I'm glad I'm a little black bug floating in the water"
Chirp, chirp, chirp.

Verse 4
There's a little red snake lying in the water
A little red snake doing what he oughter
He frightened the duck and the frog so bad
He ate the little bug and he said
"I'm glad I'm a little red snake lying in the water"
Sss, sss, sss.

Going To The Zoo   Words & Music by Tom Paxton.

4/4 Rhythm / Alternating thumb
See Course Book No.2 Page 23.

Moderately fast

Dad-dy's tak-ing us to the zoo to-mor-row, zoo to-mor-row,

zoo to-mor-row, Dad-dy's tak-ing us to the zoo to-mor-row,

CHORUS

we can stay all day. We're go-ing to the zoo, zoo, zoo, how a-bout

you, you, you? You can come too, too, too, we're go-ing to the

1-6.
zoo, zoo, zoo.

7.
zoo, zoo, zoo.
rall.

Verse 2
See the elephant with the long trunk swingin'
Great big ears and long trunk swingin'
Sniffin' up peanuts with the long trunk swingin'
We can stay all day.

Verse 3
See all the monkeys scritch, scritch, scratchin'
Jumpin' all around and scritch, scritch, scratchin'
Hangin' by their long tails scritch, scritch, scratchin'
We can stay all day.

Verse 4
Big black bear all huff, huff, a-puffin'
Coat's too heavy, he's huff, huff, a-puffin'
Don't get too near the huff, huff, a-puffin'
Or you won't stay all day.

Verse 5
Seals in the pool all honk, honk, honkin'
Catchin' fish and honk, honk, honkin'
Little seals honk, honk, honkin' *(high pitched voice)*
We can stay all day.

Sweet Gingerbread Man

Lyric by Alan & Marilyn Bergman. Music by Michel Legrand.

4/4 Rhythm / Bass-strum / Swing
See Course Book No.3 Page 10.

Moderately (not too fast)

Count: 1 2 & 3 & 4 &

Feel like I'm made out o' gin - ger - bread. Uh, huh, uh,

huh! Crumb pick - in', lip lick - in' gin - ger - bread. Uh,

huh, uh, huh! Can't think a - bout rain -

- y weath - er now, I've fi - nal - ly got___ my - self to - geth - er now!

Fresh out o' the pan,___ Sweet Gin - ger - bread Man!

To Coda ⊕

___ Fresh out o' the pan,___ Sweet Gin - ger - bread Man!___

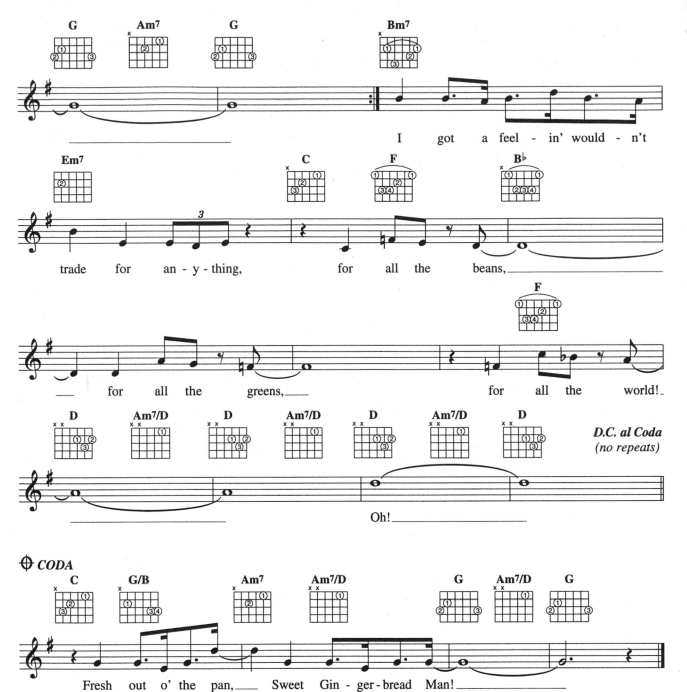

I got a feel - in' would - n't trade for an - y - thing, for all the beans, _____ for all the greens, _____ for all the world!

D.C. al Coda
(no repeats)

Oh!

⊕ *CODA*

Fresh out o' the pan, _____ Sweet Gin - ger - bread Man! _____

Verse 2
Twirlin' a cane o' peppermint
Uh, huh, uh, huh!
Nice icky, hand sticky peppermint!
Uh, huh, uh, huh!
Spun sugary cloud I'm floatin' on
Sun's spreadin' my suit o' sugar coatin' on
All tasty and tan, Sweet Gingerbread Man!
Fresh out o' the pan, Sweet Gingerbread Man!

Verse 3 (on D.C.)
Feel like I'm made out o' gingerbread
Uh, huh, uh, huh!
Crumb pickin', lip lickin' gingerbread
Uh, huh, uh, huh!
Can't think about rainy weather now
I've finally got myself together now!
All tasty and tan, Sweet Gingerbread Man!
Fresh out o' the pan, Sweet Gingerbread Man!

El Condor Pasa (If I Could)
Musical Arrangement by J. Milchberg & D. Robles. English Lyric by Paul Simon.

4/4 Rhythm / Syncopated arpeggio
See Course Book No.3 Page 16.

Think of as two arpeggio patterns joined together per bar.

Slowly

I'd ra-ther be a spar-row than a snail. Yes I would. If I

could, I sure-ly would._____ Hm_____ I'd

ra-ther be a ham-mer than a nail. Yes I would. If I on-ly

could,_____ I sure-ly would._____ Hm_____ A-

way, I'd rath-er sail a-way_____ Like a swan that's here and

gone. A man gets tied up to the ground, He gives the world its sad-dest

sound,   its sad-dest   sound._____   I'd

ra-ther be a for-est than a   street.   Yes I   would.   If I   could,_____ I sure-ly

would._____   I'd   ra-ther feel the earth be-neath my   feet.   Yes I

would.   If I on-ly   could,_____   I sure-ly   would._____

Instrumental cue

1.

2.   rall.

Puff (The Magic Dragon)

Words & Music by Peter Yarrow & Leonard Lipton.

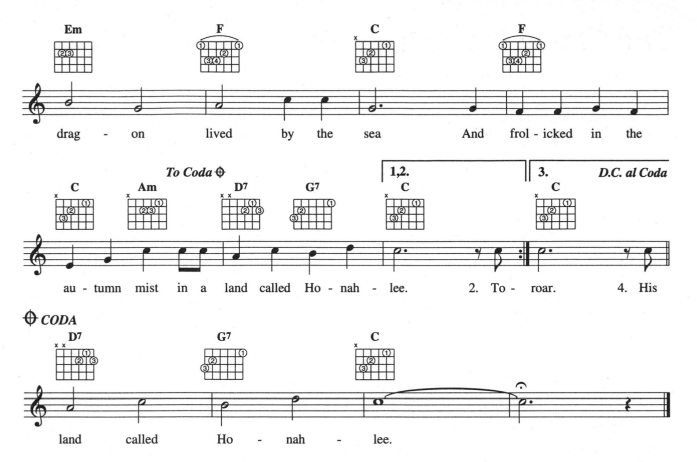

Verse 2
Together they would travel in a boat with billowed sail
Jackie kept a lookout perched on Puff's gigantic tail
Noble kings and princes would bow whene'er they came
Pirate ships would lower their flag when Puff roared out his name.

Verse 3
A dragon lives forever but not so little boys
Painted wings and giant rings make way for other toys
One grey night it happened Jackie Paper came no more
And Puff that mighty dragon he ceased his fearless roar.

Verse 4 (on D.C.)
His head was bent in sorrow, green scales fell like rain
Puff no longer went to play along the cherry lane
Without his lifelong friend, Puff could not be brave
So Puff that mighty dragon sadly slipped into his cave.

The Candy Man
Words & Music by Leslie Bricusse & Anthony Newley.

To Coda ⊕

The can - dy man can 'cause he mix - es it with love and makes the
(can - dy man can.)

1. world__ taste good._____

2. world taste good._____ The

can - dy man makes ev - 'ry - thing he bakes sat - is - fy - ing and de -

li - cious. Talk a - bout your child - hood wish - es.

D.%. al Coda
(no repeats)

You can e - ven eat the dish - es.

⊕ *CODA*

Very slowly ad lib.

world__ taste good._____ And the world tastes good 'cause the

a tempo

Rhythm

Repeat and fade

can - dy man thinks__ it should._____
rall.

The Marvellous Toy

Words & Music by Tom Paxton.

4/4 Rhythm / Alternating thumb / Strumming / Swing
See Course Book No.3 Pages 11 and 17.

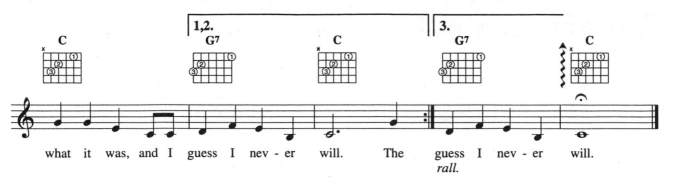

what it was, and I guess I nev - er will.   The   guess I nev - er will.
rall.

Verse 2

The first time that I picked it up I had a big surprise
For right on its bottom were two big buttons that looked like big green eyes
I first pushed one and then the other, and then I twisted its lid
And when I set it down again, this is what it did.

Chorus 2

It first marched left and then marched right and then it marched under a chair
And when I looked where it had gone, it wasn't even there!
I started to sob and my daddy laughed, for he knew what I would find
When I turned around, my marvellous toy, chugging from behind.

Verse 3

Well the years have gone too quickly, it seems, I have my own little boy
And yesterday I gave to him my marvellous little toy
His eyes nearly popped right out of his head and he gave a squeal of glee
Neither one of us knows just what it is, but he loves it, just like me.

Chorus 3

It still goes "Zip" when it moves and "Bop" when it stops
And "Whirr" when it stands still
I never knew just what it was
And I guess I never will.

The Unicorn

Words & Music by Shel Silverstein.

Book 3

4/4 Rhythm / Syncopated arpeggio / Swing
See Course Book No.3 Pages 16 and 17.

© Copyright 1962 & 1968 by Hollis Music Incorporated, USA.
All rights for the British Commonwealth of Nations (excluding Canada &
Australasia) & the Republic of Eire controlled by TRO Essex Music Limited,
Suite 2.07, Plaza 535 Kings Road, London SW10.
All Rights Reserved. International Copyright Secured.

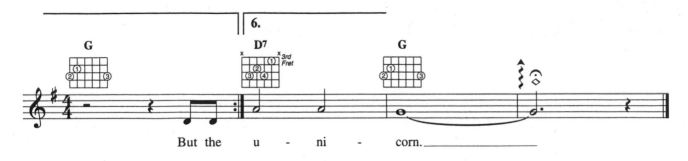

Verse 2
But the Lord seen some sinnin' and it caused Him pain
He says "Stand back, I'm gonna make it rain
So hey, Brother Noah, I'll tell you what to do
Go and build me a floating zoo."

Chorus 2
And you take two alligators and a couple of geese
Two hump back camels and two chimpanzees
Two cats, two rats, two elephants, but as sure as you're born
Noah don't forget my unicorns.

Verse 3
Now Noah was there and he answered the callin'
And he finished up the ark as the rain started fallin'
Then he marched in the animals two by two
And he sung out as they went through.

Chorus 3
"Hey Lord, I got two alligators and a couple of geese
Two hump back camels and two chimpanzees
Two cats, two rats, two elephants, but as sure as you're born
Lord, I just don't see your unicorns."

Verse 4
Well, Noah looked out through the drivin' rain
But the unicorns was hidin' playin' silly games
They were kickin' and a splashin' while the rain was pourin'
Oh them foolish unicorns.

Chorus 4
"And you take two alligators and a couple of geese
Two hump back camels and two chimpanzees
Two cats, two rats, two elephants, but as sure as you're born
Noah don't you forget my unicorns."

Verse 5
Then the ducks started duckin' and the snakes started snakin'
And the elephants started elephantin' and the boat started shakin'
The mice started squeakin' and the lions started roarin'
And everyone's aboard but them unicorns.

Chorus 5
I mean the two alligators and the couple of geese
The hump back camels and the chimpanzees
Noah cried, "Close the door 'cause the rain is pourin'
And we just can't wait for them unicorns."

Verse 6
And then the ark started movin' and it drifted with the tide
And the unicorns looked up from the rock and cried
And the water came up and sort of floated them away
That's why you've never seen a unicorn to this day.

Chorus 6
You'll see a lot of alligators and whole mass of geese
You'll see hump back camels and chimpanzees
You'll see cats and rats and elephants but sure as you're born
You're never gonna see no unicorn.

You're A Pink Toothbrush

Words & Music by Ralph Ruvin, Bob Halfin & Harold Irving.

4/4 Rhythm / Bass-strum / Swing
See Course Book No.3 Page 11.

On %
You're a pink toothbrush
I'm a blue toothbrush
Won't you marry me in haste?
I'll be true toothbrush
Just to you toothbrush
When we both use the same toothpaste.

Nellie The Elephant
Words by Ralph Butler. Music by Peter Hart.

6/8 Rhythm / Mixed arpeggios and pinches
See Course Book No.4 Page 29.

Pattern for Verses

Count: 1 2 3 4 5 6 1 2 3 4 5 6

Pattern for Choruses

Count: 1 2 3 4 5 6 1 2 3 4 5 6

Moderately

To Bom - bay a trav - ell - ing cir - cus came, they

brought an in - tell - i - gent el - e - phant, and Nel - lie was her name. _____

One dark night, she slipped her ir - on chain and

off she ran to Hin - du - stan and was nev - er seen a - gain.

CHORUS Faster

Play strum pattern

Nel - lie the el - e - phant packed her trunk and said good - bye to the cir - cus,

off she went with a trump-et-y-trump, Trump! Trump! Trump! Now

Nel-lie the el-e-phant packed her trunk and trun-dled back to the jun-gle,

off she went with a trum-pe-ty-trump, Trump! Trump! Trump!

Trump! Trump! Trump! (Continue chorus pattern)

Nel-lie the el-e-phant packed her trunk and said good-bye to the cir-cus,

off she went with a trum-pe-ty-trump, Trump! Trump! Trump! Now

Nel-lie the el-e-phant packed her trunk and trun-dled back to the jun-gle,

Verse 2
Night by night
She danced to the circus band
When Nellie was leading the big parade
She looked so proud and grand.
No more tricks
For Nellie to perform
They taught her how to take a bow
And she took the crowd by storm.

Achy Breaky Heart
Words & Music by Don Von Tress.

4/4 Rhythm / Strumming / Damping strings
See Course Book No.4 Page 11.

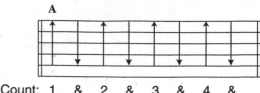

Moderately

You can tell the world you ne-ver was my girl, you can burn my clothes up when I'm gone.

You can tell your friends just what a fool I've been and laugh and joke a-bout me on the phone.

You can tell my arms go back to the farm, you can tell my feet to hit the floor, or you can tell my lips to tell my fin-ger tips they won't be reach-ing out for you no

CHORUS

more. But don't tell my heart, my a-chy break-y heart, I

Verse 2
You can tell your ma I moved to Arkansas
You can tell your dog to bite my leg
Or tell your brother Cliff whose fist can tell my lip
That he never really liked me anyway
Or tell your Aunt Louise, tell anything you please
Myself already knows I'm not okay
Or you can tell my eyes to watch out for my mind
It might be walking out on me today.

Morning Has Broken

Words by Eleanor Farjeon. Music by Cat Stevens.

4/4 Rhythm / Arpeggios with embellishments
See Course Book No.4 Pages 16 – 27.

GUITAR ACCOMPANIMENT

0 = open string

Moderately

Moderately

Morn - ing has bro - ken like the first morn -

ing, Black - bird has spok - en like the first

bird._____ Praise for the sing - ing,

Praise for the morn - ing, Praise for them

spring - ing fresh from the world_____

1,2. Csus⁴/F C/E G⁷ C

3. Csus⁴/F C/E G⁷ C

Verse 2
Sweet the rain's new fall
Sunlit from heaven
Like the first dew fall
On the first grass
Praise for the sweetness
Of the wet garden
Sprung in completeness
Where His feet pass.

Verse 3
Mine is the sun
Mine is the morning
Born of the one light
Eden saw play
Praise with elation
Praise ev'ry morning
God's recreation
Of the new day.

Scarborough Fair Traditional.

3/4 Rhythm / Arpeggios and embellishments
See Course Book No.4 Pages 16-22

GUITAR ACCOMPANIMENT

CAPO 2nd FRET   o = open string

Moderately

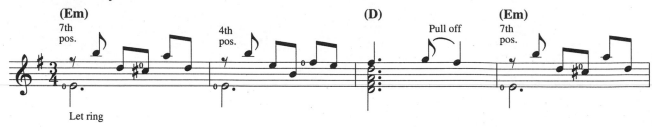

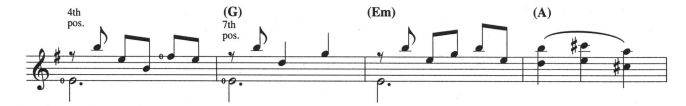

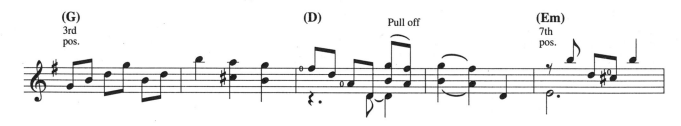

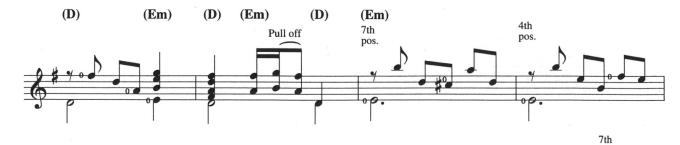

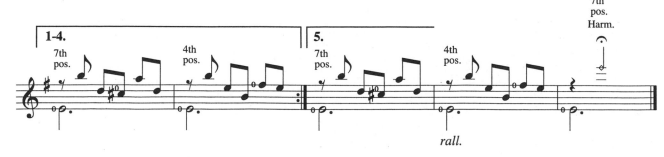

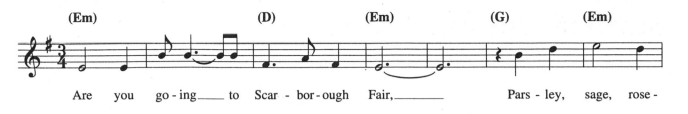

Are you go-ing___ to Scar-bor-ough Fair,_____ Pars-ley, sage, rose-

ma-ry and thyme._____ Re-mem-ber me to

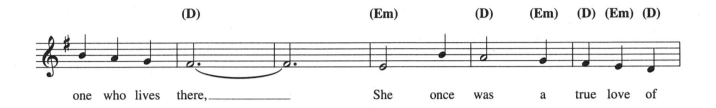

one who lives there,_____ She once was a true love of

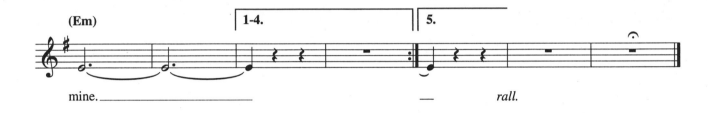

mine._____ — *rall.*

Verse 2
Tell her to make me a cambric shirt
Parsley, sage, rosemary and thyme
Without no seams nor needlework
Then she'll be a true love of mine.

Verse 3
Tell her to find me an acre of land
Parsley, sage, rosemary and thyme
Behind the salt water and the sea strands
Then she'll be a true love of mine.

Verse 4
Tell her to reap it with a sickle of leather
Parsley, sage, rosemary and thyme
And gather it all in a bunch of heather
Then she'll be a true love of mine.

Verse 5
Are you going to Scarborough Fair
Parsley, sage, rosemary and thyme
Remember me to one who lives there
She once was a true love of mine.

English Country Garden Words & Music by Robert M. Jordan.

4/4 Rhythm / Chordal accompaniment with embellishments and fills
See Course Book No.4 Pages 18 and 27.

GUITAR ACCOMPANIMENT

o = open string

Moderately

Verse 2
How many insects find their home
In an English country garden
I'll tell you now of some of them I know
And those I miss, I hope you'll pardon.

Dragonflies, moths and bees
Spiders falling from the trees
Butterflies sway in the mild gentle breeze
There are hedgehogs that roam
And little gnomes
In an English country garden.

Verse 3
How many songbirds make their nests
In an English country garden
I'll tell you now of some of them I know
And those I miss, I hope you'll pardon.

Babbling coo-coo-ing doves
Robins and the warbling thrush
Bluebird, lark, finch and nightingale
We all smile in spring
When birds all start to sing
In an English country garden.

Book 4

If I Had A Hammer
Words & Music by Lee Hays & Pete Seeger.

4/4 Rhythm / Strumming / Partially damping strings
with accent on the 2nd upstroke
See Course Book No.4 Page 11.

Verse 2

If I had a bell, I'd ring it in the morning
I'd ring it in the ev'ning all over this land
I'd ring out danger
I'd ring out a warning
I'd ring out love between all my brothers
All over this land.

Verse 3

If I had a song, I'd sing it in the morning
I'd sing it in the ev'ning all over this land
I'd sing out danger
I'd sing out a warning
I'd sing out love between all my brothers
All over this land.

Verse 4

Well I got a hammer, and I've got a bell
And I've got a song all over this land
It's the hammer of justice
It's the bell of freedom
It's the song about love between brothers and sisters
All over this land.

03/06 (5814)